BED AND BORED

BED AND BORED

Written and illustrated by
LAWRENCE LARIAR

DODD, MEAD & COMPANY

New York

1958

To

my son

STEVE

HUMOR BOOKS BY LAWRENCE LARIAR

FOREWORD

The last time I went to the hospital the operation was a success, but the patient nearly died—of boredom!

During my convalescent period, I made the following startling discoveries about hospital rooms:

1. In my room, on the ceiling above my head, I counted 798 assorted cracks in the plaster. Of this total, exactly 125 of the cracks ran from north to south.

2. During visiting hours I counted 187 guests. Most of these charmers shook their heads at me sadly. The others gleefully told me about their operations, discussed the recent demise of close friends and relatives or sat quietly by, nibbling the fruit and candy they had brought me.

3. Alone in my room, I saw the following on the hospital television set:

67 Western movies in which the hero finally gallops off into the sunset, leaving the girl behind.

84 Western movies in which the hero finally gallops off into the sunset, taking the girl with him.

86 Western movies of the "adult" variety, in which the hero leaves the girl, leaves his horse, and runs off to see a psychiatrist.

As a result of this research in boredom, I was determined to create a book guaranteed to offer pleasure and interest to anybody too weak to strike out against the bores mentioned above. Here, then, is an original assortment of puzzles and pastimes, all of them pictorial, all of them stimulating and amusing.

The next time you go to visit a sick friend in the hospital, do him a favor and bring him this book.

Then, do him another favor and—go home!

LAWRENCE LARIAR

Freeport, N. Y.

KISS ME QUICK

The sailor's problem in the picture above is no hornpipe! Starting from the X, which route would you take so that you could kiss each of the pretty babes and return to the X the shortest way possible? No fair going back over a line. You should make the correct trip after deliberating five minutes. Check your final decision with the correct answer on page 124.

QUICK PICK

Mrs. Friditch wants to buy every item in the window, but Mr. Friditch won't stand for it. He tells her he'll let her have fifty dollars if she can find the only way to spend just that amount of money on any group of items in less than half a minute. Can you help his little woman? You should crack this one in less than the blink of an eye. If you can't, you'll find the solution on page 127.

10

THE EIGHT WOLVES

The eight assorted vulpine characters above are being held away from the cute demoiselle by invisible lines, none of which touches any part of any head. Allow yourself two minutes to put these wolves where they belong, using the fewest straight lines. You'll find the solution on page 121.

THE ROCKET FUEL PROBLEM

The United States Government, caught in a missile race with Russia, embarked on its most ambitious project—a new rocket to be aimed at the moon. To preserve strictest secrecy, the engineers decided to build this space monster on a high crag deep in the Rocky Mountains. This plateau was separated from the nearest ridge by a canyon a half-mile wide and two miles deep.

At the conclusion of the actual construction of the great rocket, a bridge was built. This bridge, designed for security, was created to hold a maximum weight of 175 pounds—and not one ounce more.

On the day of the launching a crisis arose. The secret fuel had been forgotten! This fuel was contained in three balls—each of which weighed exactly two pounds. Somebody had to carry these fuel balls across the bridge. This meant that the man who carried the balls of fuel could weigh no more than 169 pounds—or the bridge would collapse.

Only one man was found who came close to the required weight, but even he was overweight, tipping the scales at 170 pounds.

Yet he was able to carry the all important fuel across the ravine while the officials gaped and stared in amazement.

Can you figure out how this talented young man did the job?

(Solution on page 122)

CANOE UPSET

Here's a quickie for all lovers of the 30 second type of mystifiers. Beginning at the lower left hand ribbon ("It was ....) continue the sentence by filling in the gap with one word. This word will make sense as you round the picture and hit it again before leaving the square on the ribbon at the right. Ready? Remember now — only 30 seconds on this one. If you can't get it you'll find the solution on page 122.

ADJECTIVITY

Everybody knows that the adjective describing the snake above would be "serpentine." But how about the other ten? You should be able to place five of the adjectives in their correct places in less than twenty seconds — and if you really know your dictionary you can guess all ten of 'em. A score of seven correct is average. Try to top it — and if you can't, turn to page 127 for the solutions.

HOW TO PLAY THE SPLITWORD GAME

The diagram on the next page was created to help you in your enjoyment of SPLIT-WORDS. The game is simple — you are asked only to break down each problem pair of words (BASHFUL BERTIE) and list all the smaller words you find. Use the first column for 4-letter words, the next for 5-letter items and the last for larger ones and extra space. (See next page.)

Follow these rules: —

1. Smallest words must have four letters. Use no plurals. (This eliminates all three-letter word forms.) Use no words that add an S to a three-letter verb. (This kills such words as SITS, RUNS, etc.)

2. Use only the noun OR the verb for words having same meaning. Thus, you can use LOSE but not LOSER, MAKE but not MAKER, etc.

3. Use only one form for each word meaning. Thus, HUNGER or HUNGERED, RATE or RATED, etc.

4. When two people are playing the game, scores should be set up allowing a bonus for large words. Let the dictionary be your guide in settling disputes. Obsolete words do not count. Proper names are out, too. A time limit should be set for each game.

The SPLITWORD puzzles in this book have been planned to give you the widest variety of sport for this type of game. Get started on the one directly opposite to see what we mean.

"All right, I'll get you a new spring outfit — but that's blackmail!"

BALE	BRASH	BERATE
BILE	BLEAT	
BELT	BLURT	
flat		
shaft		
shift		
shoal		
shut		
slit		
sit		
sat		
s.		

BASHFUL BERTIE

SPLITWORD PUZZLE

Expert word breakers will find little difficulty with BASHFUL BERTIE. An average score is 40 words in ten minutes, but you should be able to do well over 40 if you're on your toes. Score four words for five-letter words, six words for six-letter words.

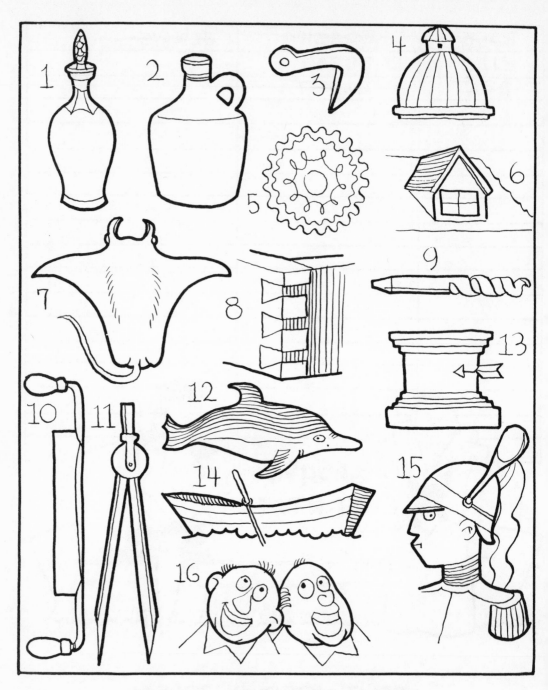

"D" IS FOR DECANTER

"D" is for DIFFICULT, too — and this page of objects will prove baffling for even the most erudite puzzlers. Each item on the page begins with the letter D — and if you can guess eight of them correctly in ten minutes, your score is average. Ten right is an excellent score — and anything over ten will come from college professors. The answers are on page 123.

IDIOT'S DELIGHT

Here's a ten minute pastime that should drive you crazy in six and one half minutes. The idea is simple: — just follow the arrow in and start with the letter "I". Go on from there to spell out a sentence. Which sentence? The one we want you to spell, of course. There is a very important clue hidden on this page. Find it, and — it should be easy to do this! Solution on page 114.

HOW TO DO A REBUS

A rebus is a riddle using pictures to express words and phrases. In this type of puzzle, the creator attempts to outwit the puzzler by expressing himself in simple pictures and avoiding letters as much as possible.

For example, this short rebus uses two letters and one picture and yet gives you only two words: —

Got it? The rebus says: — FEAR NOUGHT.

Here's one that's a bit more difficult. See if you can decode it in less than two minutes: —

Did you get it? It says, simply: — SO LONG, LINDA, (L in DA), IT'S A LITTLE TOO LONG TO WAIT FOR YOU (8 4 U) I'LL BE (Isle B) SEEING U BEFORE THE SEASON (C's on) IS OVER, ALEX (LX).

Remember that you are asked to use your ingenuity when solving a rebus. Watch for tricky combinations of presentation such as words and letters, letters and pictures, and words over words. Try these: —

¹ **Put** OOOOOOOO   ² STAND / ing   3 (thumb ED)   4 ING / h (ear)

Number 1 is POTATOES. (put 8 o's). Number 2 is UNDERSTANDING. Number 3 is UNDERHANDED. Number 4 is OVERHEARING.

Ready to go? Try your skill at the first puzzle in the book using the rebus. This one is easy — there are tougher ones ahead.

THE BALL AND CHAIN PUZZLE

Anxious Adolph and his bride-to-be have been stopped in their tracks on the way to the marriage depot by a rebus sign put there by a member of The Anti-Marriage Society of South Flatbush. Will Adolph decipher the message before he gets his license? Can you? The time limit for both messages is three minutes and fifteen seconds. (The message on the arrow reads — Detour!) This should be a cinch for all married men. For the solutions, turn to page 117.

HOW FUNNY ARE YOU?

The cartoon above appeared originally with a gag line beneath it. Are you clever enough to guess which of the following lines matches the cartoon? Only one of these is correct:—

1. "I hurt it kicking sailors out of my living room!"
2. "You ought to see the other guy!"
3. "If you must know — it fell off a desk!"
4. "I can't kick — the operation was a success!"
5. "Wait'll I get my hands on Doctor Werner!"
6. "It's an ingrown toe nail."

(Solution on page 126)

THE MALVERNE MAZE

This should be a snap for all suburban dwellers. Your problem is simple: — starting from the bottom line of the frame around Malverne, you must proceed to the top line of the frame in the fewest possible straight line moves. On the way up there you must not touch any house or tree. Can you make the trip in less than half a minute? You should, if you follow the straight and narrow. For the correct route, turn to page 127.

HOW TO DO
THE WORD CHANGE PUZZLE

A favorite of puzzle makers for years, the Word Change Puzzle is still near the tops in entertainment both for solvers and creators. Here's the way a word change works: — you are asked to change the word GIRL to MAID in seven moves. This means that you must make the change by altering one letter for each new word down the line. Thus, you'd change GIRL to MAID this way: — GIRL, GIRD, BIRD, BARD, LARD, LAID, MAID.

Now — can you change HEAD to FOOT? It can be done this way: — HEAD, HERD, HARE, FARE, FORE, FORT, FOOT. Can you find a shorter route from HEAD to FOOT?

In the following WORD CHANGE PUZZLES you will be given pictorial clues to help you along the way. Observe the time limit for each puzzle of this type.

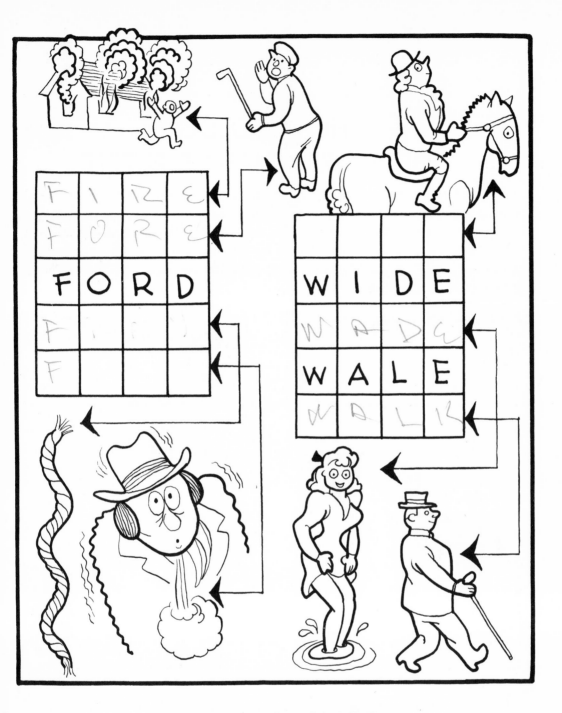

SMALL CHANGE

Here's a very simple pair of word changes, to give you a good start in the sport. The one on the left changes the top word by using a new letter to illustrate each sketch. Let the word FORD stand. On the right, the words WIDE and WALE also stand untouched. Do both in five minutes or less. Answers on page 128.

CROSS PICTURE PUZZLE

You can solve this crossword puzzle completely, by transposing the rebus clues from the other page to their proper places on this side. The letters in the boxes above remain where they are. Allow yourself just five minutes to do this one. And in case of trouble, you'll find the complete solution on page 117.

27

ANAGRAMS AND HOW TO SOLVE THEM

Webster says: — "An anagram is a word or phrase made by transposing the letters of another word or phrase." As usual, the old boy's right. Anagrams are old stuff in puzzle history, but they're still popular because they're fun to create and more fun to solve.

What do they look like? Let's take one apart. If you saw the words: — ALIKE, A RAW SLIP SHEEP and were told that these words form the name of a famous literary genius when rearranged, a little work with the old bean would soon transpose these words into WILLIAM SHAKESPEARE. LET MAN LOVE, when rearranged, becomes MALEVOLENT.

Got it? Now try the puzzle on the next page.

"Don't be alarmed, Mrs. Tucker—I've just GOT to have a few minutes sleep!"

"Has your father left for work yet, dear?"

MORNING MYSTERY

If you know your anagram apples you'll be able to pull apart O MA PA RAN and rebuild it into a bonafide word in less than one minute. The finished word means: — "a comprehensive presentation of a subject." If that isn''t enough to guide you, turn for your solution to page 128.

FIGURE IT

Minnie the model is surrounded by pictorial representations of parts of her gorgeous body. In all, there are 29 simple illustrations to solve. Can you figure 'em out in less than five minutes? If you can, take a few added moments to try the more complicated rebus she's carrying. (It's an ad for Minnie's services). Do both these problems in under ten minutes. In case of trouble, turn for the solutions to page 118.

"T" IS FOR TURNBUCKLE

— And the turnbuckle is picture number 1 in the group above. All the other objects, too, begin with the same letter — "T". Allow yourself ten minutes to see how many of these you can guess correctly. Ten correct is excellent. Eight right is good. Six is average. And you'll find the correct answers on page 121.

TWO IS COMPANY

These little pictures should give you clues to some famous pairs well known to you. For instance, the first picture illustrates: — Mutt and Jeff. Jeff is missing, of course, as are all the other halves of each pair. If you can guess twelve of these in ten minutes, your score is perfect. Eight correct is average. For the solutions, page 124.

1. Which one of these characters is a ZOUAVE?

A   B   C   D

2. Check which of these is a YOUNKER?

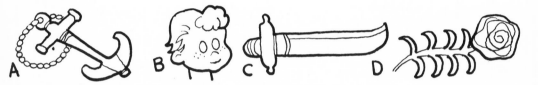

A   B   C   D

3. A DIPSOMANIAC would crave which of these?

A   B   C RYE   D   E

4. Which of these creatures is a WAMPUS?

A   B   C   D

Think twice before checking your choice on these. Then, walk, do not run, to the answers — on page 123.

DICTIONARY DOUBLE TALK

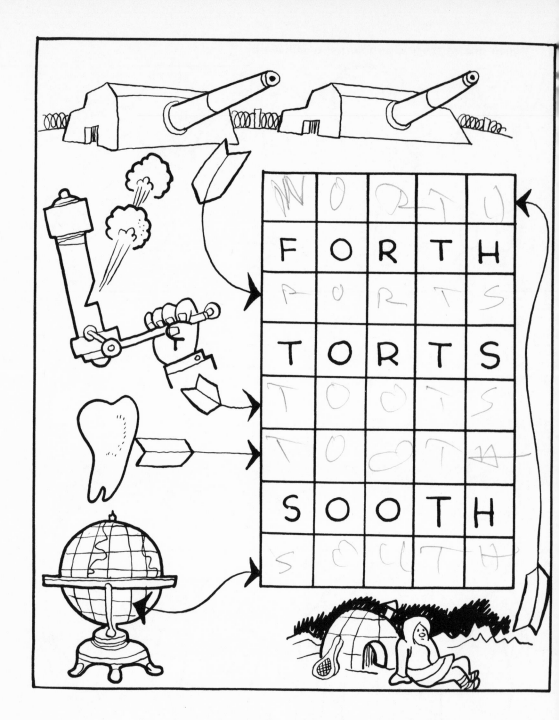

A CHANGE OF CLIMATE

This simple twister should take exactly three minutes. The five missing words are illustrated in the small pictures. Each word change is brought about by changing only one letter in each word as you go along. Leave the words FORTH, TORTS and SOOTH as they are. The solution is on page 128.

1 Select the HEDDLE from the items below: —

2. Which of these people would use PARGET?

3. Point out the INION from among these: —

4. One of these might be a KOORAJONG. Which one?

Solutions on page 124

DICTIONARY DOUBLE TALK

35

A NINE MOVE WORD CHANGE

This one should take you no longer than five minutes, and a crack word mechanic can do the job in less than three. Each word is illustrated by a picture. Each change is only a one letter change. The word FAST stays put. The solution to this one is on page 128.

"G" IS FOR GABLE

— And we don't mean Clark. The first picture is a gable — and all the others, too, begin with the letter "G". This group isn't tough at all — allowing yourself ten minutes you should be able to guess ten of 'em correctly for a good score. Find fourteen and your score is excellent. Under ten (not below six) is average. Solutions on page 121.

"Junior's picking up words fast now — he said 'Wow!' to the nurse today!"

JUNIOR WOLF

Anagramasters will find little difficulty in reforming MY SUN HER MATCH so that it becomes one word meaning: — "a *flower.*" Got it? Now try A CUTE CALL, which will form a word meaning: — "*to reckon.*" Par is five minutes for both of these words. In case of difficulty, walk, do not run, to the solution on page 120.

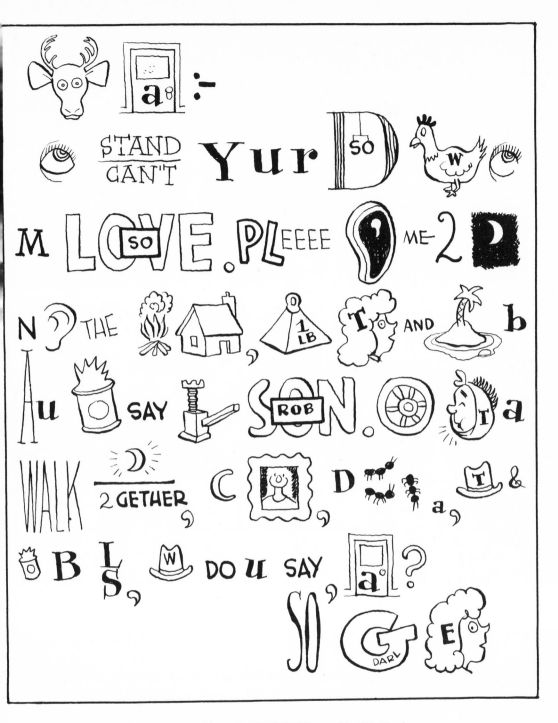

TAKE A LETTER, DORA

Here's a lovenote sent recently to Dora Dishface, by her ardent wooer, Harry Hinkledooper. Harry is a fiend about the rebus — and his entire letter may be simply deciphered by solving each little picture puzzle as it comes along. You should translate this in less than ten minutes. For the solution, turn to page 119.

AN EIGHT MOVE WORD CHANGE

Here's a fairly simple puzzle for those who like their problems quick and pointed. The arrows show you where each four letter word belongs. The word GOAD is in its proper place. Change only one letter of each word as you move down the boxes. You should solve this one in less than three minutes. The solution is on page 113.

MURDER FOR MYOPIA

Here is a fancy bit of threadwork tossed off by the author after an attack of the screaming meemies. The criss-cross maze of pen and ink above is absolutely meaningless unless you can discover the two hidden heads. One head is that of a miss — the other, a male. And a miss is as good as a male in this one, because both are hard to find. Let the eyes guide you, and if you find yourself groggy after two minutes, turn for the solution to page 122.

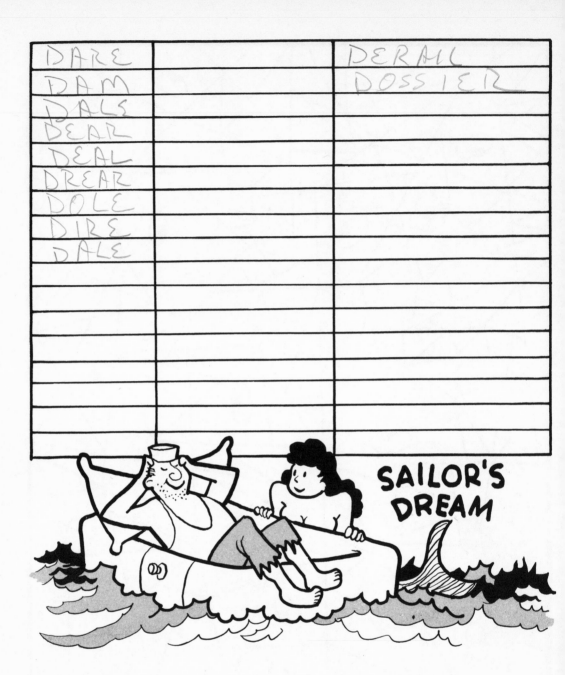

DARE		DERAIL
DAM		DOSSIER
DALS		
DEAR		
DEAL		
DREAR		
DOLE		
DIRE		
DALE		

SAILOR'S DREAM

SPLIT WORD PUZZLE

How muny words can you get out of this SAILOR'S DREAM? If you can top 45 in ten minutes, you're hitting par. Experts will do much better, especially in the five and six word department. Count two words for every five letter item discovered. Allow three words for each six-letter word. No plurals.

42

"M" IS FOR MACHETE

Every other object on this page begins with the same letter — "M". See how many of these you can jot down correctly in fifteen minutes. Only a mastermind could guess all of 'em in that time. If you hit twelve, your score is excellent. Eight correct is good. Six is average. You'll find the solutions on page 119.

"Good gentlemen I've got a catch but anyway lucky and it was just a job!"

SCRAMBLED CORN

The gag line above doesn't make much sense — or nonsense. The words have been scrambled so that it should take you a few minutes to set them in their correct order. Study the picture a bit before beginning your job. (Clue: — the manpower shortage in baseball.)

If you can't make any headway with this one after three minutes, turn for the solution to page 127.

1. If you wanted a RAMUS, which would you pick?

2. Check which of these items is a REEVE: —

3. Careful, now — which of these is a RIGOL?

4. Select the object resembling a BEGUM: —

5. In which of these objects would you use a DOWEL PIN?

6. One of these sports uses a WAILING WALL: —

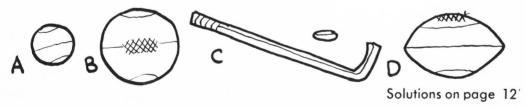

Solutions on page 12

DICTIONARY DOUBLE TALK

HOW TO SOLVE A CRYPTOGAG

Does the double talk on the next page confuse you? You've never solved a cryptogram? They're not too tough, if you know how they're done.

Cryptographers create their puzzles by simply substituting various letters for the originals. In other words, they begin by saying: — A will be X, B will be P, C will be E — and so on. By substituting these fictitious letters for each of the original letters, a cryptogram is born.

Your job then, is to unscramble the substitutions and recreate the original sentence. This isn't too difficult if you remember that the vowels — A, E, I, O, U, comprise about 40 per cent of all letters in words. The next most common letters are N, R, S, T and L. All others are used less often. (J, X, Z, Q and K, are the least used letters in the alphabet.)

With this in mind, you can approach any cryptogram with confidence. You should remember, too, that the easiest way to break down this type of puzzle is to tackle the small words first, especially the one, two and three letter words. Once you've determined that GHQ means THE, for instance, you have the use of the letter E, which can immediately be placed into position wherever Q appears.

You'll notice that the CRYPTOGAG on the opposite page contains quite a few short words. There are only two one letter words in the English language: — "A" and "I". With this to guide you, it shouldn't be too hard to unscramble this first CRYPTOGAG. The others will be tougher. But the pictures should help you along the way, because each CRYPTOGAG is a real gag line for the cartoon above it.

CRYPTOGAG

"MADAM COME HARROMP DOC CU MICA — TYBH EABJMOBA CA HX DOC!!"

What is the cute doll saying to the receptionist? We'll give you a hint — she wants to get in to see the boss. For the pretty speech she's making, you'll have to resort to cryptography to decode the mysterious gag line. Remember that two-letter words are important — and there are three of 'em up there. Try this for thirty minutes — and if you fail — you'll find the gag line on page 119.

"So you want your ring back, eh? All right — take your pick!"

SUITOR'S SURPRISE

Overcome by emotion while doing the tragic cartoon above, the artist made many, many mistakes. Can you find all of them after three minutes of careful scrutiny? After you've made your list, check your findings with the complete solution on page 125.

THE BRUSHOFF REBUS

Here's a little note from a miss named Dora, to her boy friend Harry, the rebus fancier.

Your problem is to decode these picture signals and translate the entire letter in less than fifteen minutes. A crack rebus man solved this one in less than five minutes, believe it or not.

The correct answer is on page 116.

"Cone I tog redstat, I dofun I dontluc post!"

ANAGRAMGAG

Each word in the gag line above has been reformed into an anagram. The words are in their proper order. Your job is to rearrange the letters in each word until they make sense — and nonsense. (The first word is "Once".) Your only clue to the gag is the fact that the sculptor is nuts about rabbits. After three minutes, if you haven't snagged the correct gag line, turn for your solution to page 123.

THE NAUGHTICAL NOUGHTS

Here's another speed test: — In less than one minute can you add four straight lines to the six zeros near the sailor to describe him? In the same minute, add four straight lines to the zeros under the angelic dog to form two words describing the mutt. Got it? If not — turn for your answer to page 128.

THE PUZZLE OF THE HOLLYWOOD STARLETS

The press agent for a major Hollywood studio recently startled the movie world by setting up a fantastic publicity stunt. He announced that his studio would soon select new stars. Then he challenged a famous reporter to visit three young prospects and try to guess which one of them had achieved star status.

"It should be easy," he said. "The true stars can only tell you the truth. Starlets are all liars."

The reporter accepted the challenge. He was escorted to the side of a giant waterfall where all three girls were working in the same picture. They awaited him on the other side of the rushing torrent.

The reporter shouted across the stream: "You, over there! Are you a starlet or a star?"

But the first girl's answer was lost in the great noise of the cascading waterfall.

The second girl heard the question and shouted: "She says she's a star. She is a star. So am I a star!"

The third girl laughed, pointing to the second.

"Don't you believe her. She's only a starlet—but I'm a real star!"

Can you solve the reporter's problem? What was the status of each girl?

(Solution on page 125)

BATHING BEAUTY

SPLIT WORD PUZZLE

Expert word splitters can get over fifty smaller words out of BATHING BEAUTY, in less than fifteen minutes. Eliminating all three-letter words, can you construct forty words without resorting to the three-letter variety? A score of forty in ten minutes is excellent. Thirty is average.

ASTIGMATIC ADDLER

The unfortunate gob standing on the poop deck has been instructed to discover the position of two important stars in this cockeyed firmament. The stars are there, somewhere, but fairly well hidden by a fog of angles. You should be able to spot the stars after a moment's study, but if you find yourself stymied you'll find the key to this one on page 123.

"C" IS FOR CADUCEUS

All the other pictures on the page begin with the letter "C", too. Only one person in a county can guess all of these items within twenty minutes after starting. If you guess ten of 'em, your knowledge of the dictionary is very good. A score of eight is average. And even five of these guessed correctly proves you no slouch. Solutions on page 128.

FIVE VERY BUSY B'S

The teacher is pointing out five wonderful rules for every good boy to follow in this tricky puzzle picture. Can you discover these rebus rules in less than three minutes? If you get stuck, the solutions are on page 122.

CRYPTOGAG

"BANVO BETCA ZTR ONFL ZTR BNCVKL VAK PTCKZ QTE HTQQKK, LFLCV ZTR?"
The gag for this cartoon should be obvious enough to help you over the hurdles with the Cryptogag. Fifteen minutes is plenty for solving this one, but if you can't, the solution's on page 127.

THE TEN TRAVELERS PUZZLE

Ten weary, footsore travelers,
All in a woeful plight,
Sought shelter at a wayside inn
One dark and stormy night.

"Nine rooms, no more," the landlord said,
"Have I to offer you.
To each of eight a single bed,
But the ninth must serve for two."

A din arose. The troubled host
Could only scratch his head,
For of those tired men no two
Would occupy one bed.

The puzzled host was soon at ease—
He was a clever man—
And so to please his guests devised
This most ingenious plan.

In room marked A two men were placed,
The third was lodged in B.
The fourth to C was then assigned,
The fifth retired to D.

In E the sixth he tucked away,
In F the seventh man,
The eighth and ninth in G and H,
And then to A he ran,

Wherein the host, as I have said,
Had laid two travelers by,
Then taking one—the tenth and last—
He lodged him safe in I.

Nine single rooms—a room for each—
Were made to serve for ten;
And this it is that puzzles me
And many wiser men.

(Solution on page 120)

"You threwc — you thmig veha dolt me you ewer grinbing
doombesy mohe to rendin!!"

ANAGRAMGAG

The little bride is pretty mad at her new husband. Can you rearrange the letters
in each word so that you'll wind up with her complete speech to him? (The words
"You — you — me — you — to — " should be left as is.) All the words are in their
correct order. All your clues to the gag are in the picture itself. If you can't solve this
one in less than two minutes, turn for your solution to page 123.

"F" IS FOR FASCES

You can have fifteen minutes to work this one out. All the objects represented begin with the letter "F" — and not too many of them are easy. If you can guess fourteen correctly, your score is excellent. Eight right means that you're average in the dictionary department. Here's a hint: — one word is used twice for two objects. Answers to this one are on page 114.

"P" IS FOR PAGODA

Can you guess the sixteen other objects on this page — all of which begin with the letter P? You should be able to guess at least eight if your knowledge of the dictionary is average. Experts will guess all seventeen, but lesser experts will be content to name thirteen. The answers are on page 113.

"Did you find a little boy who's holding on to a skirt?"

SLIP SHOWING

There are many, many mistakes in the cartoon above. Can you spot 'em all? Allow yourself five minutes to catch the artist's errors. Then turn to page 115 for the complete list and your score.

1. On which of these items would you find an ORLOP?

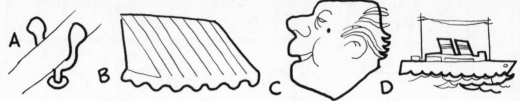

2. Check which of these looks like a NEEP: —

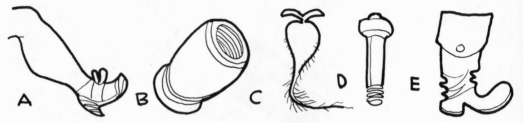

3. One of these gents is a MERCER. Which one?

4. Locate the CATENATED object below: —

Solutions — page 126

DICTIONARY DOUBLE TALK

PAIR 'EM UP

Each little picture will give you the name of one person of a famous pair. (The first picture is a rebus for "Pierrot" — Pier — O — thus the pair would be "Pierrot and Pierrette") Can you snare the other fourteen pairs? A good average score is 8 out of 15 — but careful scrutiny should net you a higher score. Answers are on page 126.

CROSS PICTURE PUZZLE

Here's a novel variation on the old crossword theme. The words and letters in the puzzle above remain just as they are. All the other words are well defined on the page to your right as simple rebuses. Solve each rebus and put your solution where it belongs above. Time limit — 10 minutes. If you score 100% you'll wind up with a completed crossword puzzle. No other clues are necessary and you'll find the correct solution on page 120.

LITERARY IMPASSE

The two thugs have walked into a major puzzle while trying to rob the safe of a famous literary agent. In order to open the contraption, they must first spell out a three letter word, using two letters from the top dial and one from the bottom. After you've solved this one, try to decipher the tricky anagram and make one word out of A RAT MIND IS ON IT. (The word means: — "*the performance of the executive duties of a business.*") Both solutions on page 124.

SPUTNIK PROBLEM

Here's an outer space problem that you should be able to solve in about three minutes. Find room for a star larger than any above—and make sure it touches none of the others. You'll find the answer on page 118.

1. Guess which of these is SEMÉ: —

2. Careful now — point out the TOD: —

3. There's a VIMEN below. Can you pick it out?

4. Which of these would be a CARLINE?

5. There's a FAL-LAL below — which is it?

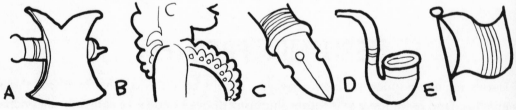

Solutions on page 124

DICTIONARY DOUBLE TALK

SPLIT SECOND MAZE

Which of the four roads will lead Sailor Sam to the house on the lower right side of the page? You should be able to find the correct path in less than thirty seconds, because this is a problem of deduction. Study the drawing carefully before making your choice. After a quick and careful survey of the picture, your choice should be obvious. Solution — page 113.

"She tog het grown benrum — bandyoy twan ot aspek ot mih?"

ANAGRAMGAG

What is the boarding house lady saying to the gals? The letters in each word have been rearranged to confuse you—but the words are in the correct order and if you rearrange the letters in each word the right way, you'll have the gag line. The correct answer is on page 126.

"I see a tall, dark and handsome gent — and I'm going out after this one *myself!*"

TIPSY GYPSY

Are you anagramatical? Test your skill on the top anagram first. IN MAGIC TALE, when rearranged, will form a word that means: — "*puzzling, inexplicable, resembling an enigma.*" IT'S NO DEMON'S ART!, will resolve itself into one word meaning: — "*manifestations.*" Pull out your stop watch and see whether you can do both of the anagrams above in less than three minutes. Solutions on page 119.

"Ska rhe fi hess tog a ridfen denam blame?"

THE MABEL MYSTERY

As quick as a flash, can you rearrange the garbled letters of each of the words above so that you'll wind up with the correct gag line? You should solve this one in less than one minute. Solution on page 113.

FROM WICHITA TO AKRON

Mr. and Mrs. Oscar Oomplaut want to start at Akron (A) and visit each of the small towns on the map before arriving at Wichita (W). Can you show Oscar how to make the trip and visit each town only once without traveling any of the roads twice? If you can, and have a minute to spare, try to guess the names of states hidden in the picture. Solutions on page 114.

GIRLY WIRLY

Scattered around the square puzzle above are the names of fifteen girls — each presented to you in simple pictures. If you can guess all fifteen in under three minutes your score is perfect. The square item in the above frame is a spelling square, containing the names of quite a few added gals. Move from one box to another and see how many you can snag. (You can move in any direction.) Answers to these on page 114.

1. One of these is UNCINATE — know which one?

2. Point out the YATAGHAN: —

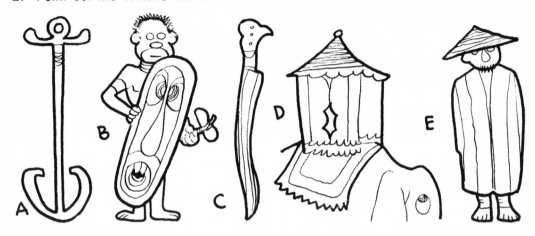

3. Which of these gents wears a KEPI?

4. Still interested? Indicate the FARTHINGALE: —

(Solutions on page 113)

DICTIONARY DOUBLE TALK

THE PROBLEM OF THE TWO DANCERS

Two very cute dancers turned up for a test in the office of a famous Broadway producer. Both were asked the usual background questions, during which the following startling facts were discovered:

Each girl was named Lattimer.

Each girl was born on December 24th, 1938.

Each was born at 5673 Lena Avenue, Freeport, Long Island.

Each had a father named Ulysses Lattimer.

Each had a mother named Violet Lattimer.

The producer studied the answers carefully and then asked, "You two are sisters, aren't you?"

"We certainly are."

"And you're twins, aren't you?"

He was completely flabbergasted when they answered, "No!"

Yet, the girls told the truth, all the way through the many questions he had asked them.

How do you figure the producer a fool? Can you guess immediately the reason why they were not twins?

(Solution on page 123)

TEST YOUR FUNNY BONE

The correct gag line for this cartoon appears below. Can you pick it out? Only one line is correct, but your second and third choices will reflect your sense of humor. Compare your selections with the answers on page 126.

1. "Don't go near him — it raises his temperature!"
2. "Watch out for that pilot. He may be grounded, but he still has a cruising range of two or three feet!"
3. "He's a cavalry man — he still horses around!"
4. "Watch out for his manoeuvres — he's from the infantry!"
5. "Don't take his pulse — you'll never get your hand back!"
6. "He's a sailor — watch out for his port arm!"

THE MERMAID MEMORY QUIZ

Focus your optics on the picture above. Concentrate on each and every object pictured. Study all of them for no longer than one minute. Your problem is to try and remember as many of the assorted thingamabobs surrounding the little mermaid as you possibly can. When you've finished your study period, turn the page and prepare to be quizzed.

THE MERMAID MEMORY QUIZ

Now — got your pencil handy? Jot down on a piece of paper (or on the margin of this page) as many of the items around the mermaid as you can remember. (No fair turning back for another gander!)

If you've remembered eighteen objects — your score is perfect. (There are over twenty on the page, but even an expert couldn't recall all of 'em!) A score of twelve is average — and anything under a dozen means you looked too long at the mermaid's tail.

SPECIAL TEST FOR EXPERT MEMORIZERS

So you think the test above was a pipe? You want something really tough? All right, chum — you asked for it. Without turning back to the last page, see how many of the questions below you can answer correctly. Score — 7 correct — wow! 6 correct — elegant. 3 correct — average. 1 correct — dull normal.

1. How many tentacles has the octopus twined around the mermaid?
2. How many times is the letter "G" in the picture?
3. Is the tea kettle steaming?
4. How many fish are there in the picture?
5. What is the letter on the buoy?
6. What do the street signs on the lamp-post say?
7. How many men in the picture?
8. Did you see any smoke at all?
9. Where is the bird?
10. What letter is floating in the water?

auricle
myocardium
epidermis
conjunctiva
bronchi
digit
pharynx
peritoneum
cerebrum
ilium
denture
os

THE BODY BEAUTIFUL

Here's an interesting item for students of Latin, Greek and old Brooklyn culture. The idea is simple — just write down the part of the body suggested by each of the little words alongside the seductive wench. You should be able to guess five right, even if you never went to high school. Ten correct is smart stuff. You'll find a break-down of the Latin double talk on page 128.

1. Which of these gentlemen would use a LANCET?

2. Select the shape that reminds you of LOZENGE: —

3. A NUCHA may be found in one of these. Which?

4. Indicate which of these suggests AKIMBO: —

Solutions on page 114

DICTIONARY DOUBLE TALK

THE FOUR SAILORS PUZZLE

These four sailors are each dreaming a personal dream. Sailor "A" dreams of his sailboat — sailor "B" of his girl — sailor "C" of his home in the west of Flatbush — sailor "D" of nothing more than a plateful of turkey. Can you connect each sailor to his dream with a line and keep each line from crossing? (Lines needn't be straight.) Answer on page 116.

NUMBERS PLEASE!

Here are two mathematical manipulations for mature masters of the numbers racket. The top square is to be filled with the numbers shown so that each line in any direction in the square will total 36. The bottom square should be filled so that each line will total 34. Don't fiddle with the numbers already in the squares. They're in the right spots. Take all the time you want on these. You'll find the solutions on page 119.

GOOD HUMOR TEST

The cartoon above will get a real laugh if you can select the proper caption for it. Test your wit by selecting the correct line from the following group. Only one of these is right:

1. "We must be in the wrong house."
2. "Meet the new cook, Ed — she makes a swell little meal!"
3. "Joe — I want you to meet the little woman!"
4. "Are you sure you live in this house, Meyer?"
5. "Good things come in small packages!"

(Solution on page 128)

1. Which of these gentlemen is practising PANDICULATION?

2. It should be easy to mark the RUNDLET below: —

3. Which of the group below is a TYCOON?

4. If you wanted a TRAGUS, which of these would be it?

5. Pick out the TUSSOCK from this group: —

6. On which of the items below would you use PRUNELLA?

Answers are to be found on page 118.

DICTIONARY DOUBLE TALK

"H" IS FOR HACKSAW

Here again, all the objects on the page begin with the letter H. Ten minutes is the time limit on this one — and if you can guess twelve out of fourteen correctly, your score is tops. The average on this is eight right, altho' even five isn't hopeless. You'll find the correct answers on page 122.

"We absolutely guarantee that gown for three marriages!"

BRIDAL WAIL

The whimsical diagram above has been put together so that there are many mistakes for you to discover in the art department. Allow yourself three minutes to find all the errors. Then, check your list with the correct solutions on page 120.

THE SARONG MEMORY TEST

Stop staring at the doll and concentrate on the objects around and about her. Study these objects for a full minute and a half. Try to remember all of them, including the pickled herring the lass is carrying to her grandmaw. When the minute and a half is gone, turn the page and test your memory. (And no looking back after you've turned the page!)

THE SARONG MEMORY TEST

Now, if you're really interested in testing your powers of observation and your ability to remember — write down as many of the objects on the preceding page as you can recall.

Excluding the girl and everything she's carrying, there are seventeen assorted items surrounding the babe. If you remembered all seventeen, plus the initial on the object the girl is holding in her right hand, you have an astoundingly good memory.

If you remembered twelve of the objects, your memory is good. A score of ten objects or less means that you weren't really concentrating. (We warned you to stop gaping at the doll, didn't we?)

SPECIAL TEST FOR EXPERT GUESSERS

So you think you have a keen eye? The test was too simple for a memorizer of your caliber? Okey, chum — see how many of these questions you can answer: —

1. What is the number on the ten pin?
2. How many links on the chain?
3. What is lettered on the spark plug?
4. What is the card?
5. What is the name of the book?
6. Is the razor a safety or a double-edge type?
7. How many bulbs in the lamp?
8. Are the girl's eyes open or shut?
9. How many straps on the brief case?
10. How many objects on the page are edible?

Score: — 10 correct — genius.   7 correct — excellent.
           5 correct — good.   Under 5 — fair.

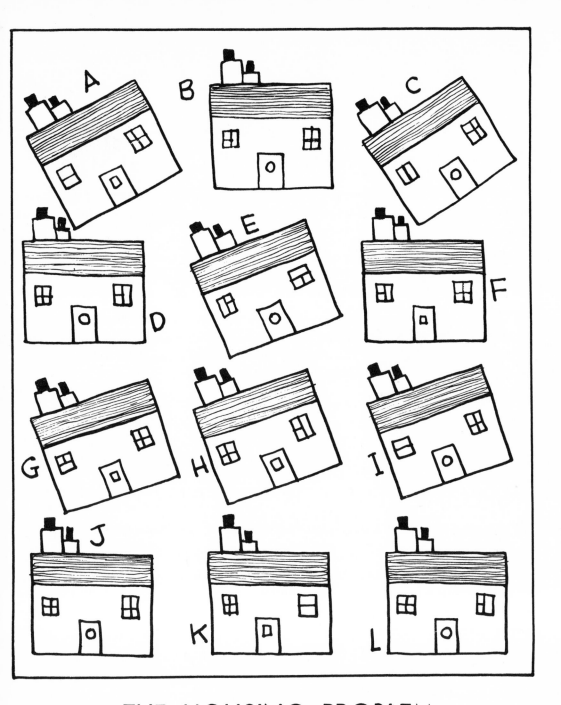

THE HOUSING PROBLEM

Here's a simple puzzle for anybody who has ever owned a five-room house with hot and cold running mortgages. Two of the dwellings pictured above are identical twins. All others are different in one way or another. Study the picture carefully and select the twins in less than one minute and a half. (Don't go counting the lines in each roof — they're meant to be the same.) Solution — page 114.

FISHERMAN'S FUN

The situation above is loaded with humor for all those who have ever gone fishing with the little woman. Listed below are six funny lines — only one of which is the correct caption for this cartoon. Test your funny bone by trying for the right title — and remember — your second and third choices are important, too. The answers are on page 127.

1. "Stop rocking the boat, Sue-— I think I've got a nibble!"
2. "You should have seen the one that just got away!"
3. "You're just imagining things, dear!"
4. "Pull up the anchor — this spot is no good!"
5. "Have you baited your hook yet, dear?"
6. "Don't be so restless — you'll get a bite soon, dear!"

SPLIT WORD PUZZLE

Here's a natural split-up: — DIVORCE ACTION. For a quick check on your abilities, allow yourself only ten minutes and see if you can top 45 words, including the four-letter variety in that time limit. Take a bonus of five words for every six-letter word found. And — can you spot the seven letter items? They're in there!

HOW FUNNY ARE YOU?

This cartoon will provoke a real chuckle only when it has the right caption beneath it. The lady straphanger is obviously saying something to the weird character in the seat—see if you can pluck her dialogue from the following lines. Only one of these is correct:

1. "Didn't I meet you in Dubuque?"
2. "Stop staring at me or I'll call a cop!"
3. "Don't I know you? Your fuzz is familiar!"
4. "Why aren't you in the movies?"
5. "George Drexler! What are you doing out of Mattewan?"

(Correct line will be found on page 127)

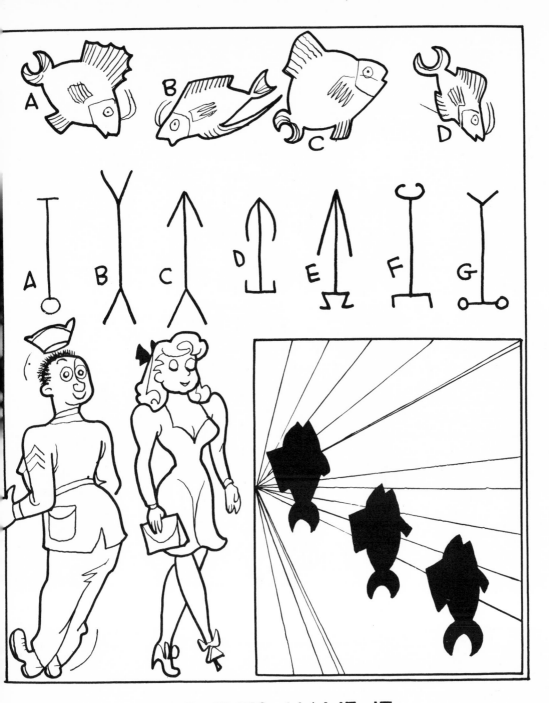

THE EYES HAVE IT

Without batting an eye, select the longest fish on the top line. Then pick the shortest. Go from there to the next eye-opener and venture a guess at the shortest line in the group (just the upright lines without the added curleycues). Now pick the longest of this group. Next, move to the right hand square and select the longest fish and the shortest one. No measuring! Allow yourself ten seconds for selections. Check your answers on page 118.

"S" IS FOR SABOT

Picture number one is a wooden shoe — but the other name for it is "sabot." All the other pictures on this page begin with the letter "S". Allowing yourself ten minutes for the page, see how many of these you know. Excellent vocabularies will find all these words. If you guess 12 your vocabulary is average. 10 is fair — and below 10, poor. Solution on page 128.

ARE YOU A GAGMAN?

The funny drawing above lacks a caption to start you laughing. Test your skill as a humorist—see if you can select the proper gag line from the list below. Only one of these is correct:

1. "Don't look now, but your wife just came in."
2. "Did I ever tell you about my operation?"
3. "That's enough politics for one night. Let's change the subject!"
4. "Do your cigarettes taste different lately?"
5. "Stop me if you've heard this one, Otto . . ."

(Solution on page 117)

"But why should I complain? This IS my old job!"

SHORE PATROL

There are over fifteen mistakes in the scene above. After you've finished laughing over the gag, take a pencil and a piece of paper and see if you can discover all of the errors in less than three minutes. The solution will be found on page 115.

SPLIT WORD PUZZLE

Here's another tough problem — a MODEST MISS in an artist's studio. You should be able to break down the little lady and arrive at 30 words for your pains. Professional breaker-uppers will do better than this, but not until at least ten minutes have flown by. Count 2 for five-letter words, 3 for six-letter words.

1. Which of these items suggests QUOIN to you?

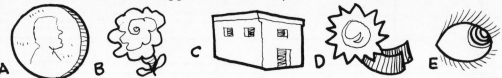

2. One of these may be afflected by BLET. Which one?

3. If you went looking for a CABRILLA, which would be it?

4. Find the DRUGGET among the things below: —

5. Easy now, which of these is a HA-HA?

6. Does any of these suggest a LONGE to you? Which?

(Solutions on page 117)

DICTIONARY DOUBLE TALK

SOMETHING TO REMEMBER

Here's another memory twister. Study the picture above for one and a half minutes. Try to concentrate on the objects surrounding the pretty miss in the bathing suit. The important thing is to remember as many objects as possible before the time is up. Then, turn the page for the memory quiz that follows.

HOW WELL DID YOU REMEMBER?

Got your pencil handy? Okey — now write down on a piece of paper (or the margin of this page) as many of the objects on the preceding page as you can recall. (no fair peeking!) If you were able to remember: —

20 objects . . . you're a genius   16 objects . . . wow!
12 objects . . . average   under 12 . . . subnormal

SPECIAL QUIZ FOR EXPERTS

If you averaged better than 12 on the test above, perhaps you'd like to try plumbing the nether depths of your memory to see if you can find the answers to this type of question.

Score: — 15 correct — genius   10 correct — wonderful
         8 correct — average   5 correct — bad

1. The girl is holding the flower in her right hand.
   True ☐   False ☐
2. How many snakes are there in the picture?
3. What is printed on the flag?
4. What is printed on the cup?
5. What letter is printed on the house?
6. There are (   ) clouds of smoke in the picture.
7. What is the letter on the man's sweater?
8. Is anything human touching the girl?
9. Is the letter below the hammer?
10. Is the candle below the leaf?
11. How many men are looking at the gal?
12. Is she returning the glances?
13. Is the screw lower than the ink bottle?
14. Around which leg of the man is the snake curled.
    Left ☐   Right ☐
15. How many leaves on the stalk the girl holds?

THE GAME OF COMPARISONS

In this simple test you are asked to supply the missing adjective in each of the above illustrated comparisons. For instance — number one is a ghost. The adjective would be "pale", since the expression is: — "Pale as a ghost." All the other pictures illustrate other expressions. Write the missing adjectives in each box. 14 correct is a fine score. 10 correct is average. Take only ten minutes for this one. Solutions on page 116.

ARE YOU A GAGMAN?

This comic drawing will be very funny if you can put the proper gag line beneath it. Match wits with the cartoon editors and see whether you can pick the right line from these. Only one of the captions is correct:

1. "Hello, Mother: Am I in time for breakfast?"
2. "But I haven't been out all night. It's only three in the morning!"
3. "I met another sailor tonight."
4. "Of course I slapped him when he kissed me — every time!"
5. "Am I too late for breakfast, Mother?"

(The solution is on page 116)

CRYPTOGAG

"NAVY SLBV YCV BARD VIA ERVAD — CPA ULV R ODCABS LB R
YFMTRDCBA YLTAEIADA!"

If you can successfully decode the above cryptograph gag line, you'll discover the dialogue the pretty damsel is using on the soldier. Follow the instructions for solving cryptograms — and, here's a hint — "R" in the above line must be either "A" or "I", since those are the only single letter words in the dictionary. The solution should be reached in thirty minutes. In case of trouble, turn to page 128.

SPLIT WORD PUZZLE

Old Abou-Ben-Rothnagle is whistling to no avail, as will you when you try to top 35 words in the breakdown of SNAKE CHARM. Expert wordbusters will take this in their stride, omitting the plurals. Five-letter words count 2 — six-letter items — 3.

1. Which of these objects is ACINIFORM?

2. Which one of these is a BERGAMOT?

3. In which of these might you find a PURLIN?

4. Careful now — point out which of these is a BIRKIE?

5. One of these four is a RICTUS — which one?

6. Which of these would be ACETOUS?

A score of three out of six lines correct is good. Check your answers with the solutions on page 122.

DICTIONARY DOUBLE TALK

ARE YOU A GAGMAN?

The cartoon above appeared originally with a gag line beneath it. Are you clever enough to guess which of the following lines matches the cartoon? Only one of these is correct:—

1. "He used to be a pawnbroker!"
2. "The judge collects them as a hobby".
3. "His eyesight is bad!"
4. "He lights 'em all for a conviction!"
5. "His brother-in-law is in the globe business."
6. "They light in technicolor!"

(The correct gag line appears on page 115)

THE AIRPLANE PROBLEM

An airplane with a crew of three is carrying three passengers from Boston to Albany. The plane's crew consists of the Captain, Pilot and Steward. Their names are Smith, Jones and Roberts, but not necessarily in this order. The three passengers are also named Smith, Jones and Roberts, but they will be referred to as Mr. Smith, Mr. Jones and Mr. Roberts.

Mr. Roberts lives in Albany. The Steward lives half way between Boston and Albany, while his namesake among the passengers lives in Boston. One of the passengers is the Steward's nearest neighbor and is related to Mr. Jones. Smith and the pilot are second cousins.

What is the Captain's name?

(Solution on page 119)

"He can't stand her voice!"

Solutions

THE MABEL MYSTERY

"Ask her if she's got a friend named Mabel?"

EIGHT MOVE WORD CHANGE

Road — GOAD — goal — coal — coil — toil — tail — rail.

DICTIONARY DOUBLE TALK

1. The little hook (C) is UNCINATE.
2. The YATAGHAN is the knife—(C).
3. The man with the KEPI is man number (C).
4. The FARTHINGALE is the lady's costume—(D).

"P"—IS FOR PAGODA

1. Pagoda. 2. Pan. 3. Panpipe. 4. Pantaloon. 5. Parallelogram. 6. Pastern. 7. Pediment. 8. Penguin. 9. Pelican. 10. Perch. 11. Pincers. 12. Pinnacle. 13. Plinth. 14. Poniard. 15. Prism. 16. Pyramids. 17. Pipefish.

SPLIT SECOND MAZE

The sailor takes route #3. This is obvious after you trace back from the end of the line at the house and find that it is a curved type of line. Each route has a line moving in a special pattern.

THE MOOMPITCHER GAME

1. FRED MARCH. 2. LUCILLE BALL. 3. RONALD COLMAN (R on LD Coalman). 4. SIMONE SIMONE. 5. FRED ASTAIRE. 6. NOEL COWARD. 7. LIONEL BARRYMORE. 8. RAY MILLAND. 9. HEDY LAMARR (head E lamb R). 10. CLIFTON WEBB. 11. ORSON WELLES. 12. WALTER PIDGEON. 13. GREER GARSON. 14. BING CROSBY.

WHAT DO YOU READ?

1. TIDE. 2. TIME. 3. FLYING ACES. 4. AMERICAN HOME. 5. CHARM. 6. THE SHADOW MAGAZINE. 7. AMERICAN (A merry can). 8. ESQUIRE (S quire). 9. ASIA (A's-ia). 10. COLLIER'S. 11. FORTUNE (4-tune). 12. LIBERTY. 13. HOLLYWOOD. 14. POPULAR MECHANICS. 15. HOUSE AND GARDEN.

DICTIONARY DOUBLE TALK

1. Only the doctor would use a LANCET.
2. The LOZENGE is the diamond shaped item (D).
3. You'll find the NUCHA in C. (Nape of the neck.)
4. The last figure (D) has his arms AKIMBO.

IDIOT'S DELIGHT

The clue to this one is the last part of the last sentence:—"IT SHOULD BE EASY TO DO THIS". Having discovered the missing sentence, it should have been child's play to waltz through the intestinal maze and spell it out.

A PUZZLE OF HEADLINES

The twins are "B" and "G". Careful study of all details, including the wrinkles on forehead and the lines under the eyes, shows that these two heads are the only twins on the page.

HOUSING PROBLEM

The twin houses are:—"D" and "L". If you checked the windows carefully, this should have been easy.

FROM WICHITA TO AKRON

Mr. Oomplaut would go from Wichita to O, V, R, N, C, H, D, J, S, P, K, E, I, B, G, M, Q, U, T, F, L — and thence into Akron.

The hidden states are: — Pennsylvania (pencil-vane-ia). Illinois. Indiana (in "D" ana). Vermont. Tennessee. Arkansas. Kansas. Ohio. Rhode Island.

GIRLY WHIRLY

1. Annabelle (N, a bell). 2. Dinah. 3. Barbara. 4. Celeste (C minus (less) T). 5. Eloise. 6. Ivy. 7. Amanda (or Hedda — (head-da)). 8. Minnie. 9. Penelope. 10. Berenice (burr in ice). 11. Hedwig. 12. Leonora. 13. Annette. 14. Justena. 15. Carmen.

The girl's names in the square: —

Dinah, Lena, Jule, Edna, Maud, Jennie, Minnie, Anna, Mary, Nan, Nancy, Jane, Mae, Judy, Hannah, Eva, Nina, Diana, Minna, Sadie, Tina, Sue.

"F" IS FOR FASCES

1. Fasces. 2. Feather. 3. Fess. 4. Fetlock. 5. Fibula. 6. Fez. 7. Ferret. 8. Fins. 9. Finial. 10. Fleur-de-lis. 11. Foil. 12. Foil. 13. Fox terrier. 14. Flounder. 15. Fid. 16. Fret. 17. Flail.

SLIP SHOWING

1. Lady's sleeves don't match (one is short).
2. Lady's shoes don't match.
3. Nor do her stockings. (One up, one rolled down.)
4. That item in the shopping bag is impossible (the man).
5. The handbag beside it has the handle upside down.
6. Sign on wall is misspelled. (Buy WAR BONDS.)
7. Carpet is tacked right up on molding of wall.
8. Ash stand is floating in midair.
9. Hey—what's a hydrant doing in the YMCA?
10. And, come to think of it, why is the dame shopping in the YMCA?
11. Man at desk has tie clipped too low.
12. LOST AND FOUND sign is out of spelling.
13. Light fixture hanging from nowhere.
14. Ditto for light.

ARE YOU A GAGMAN?

"He lights 'em all for a conviction!"

SHORE PATROL

1. Sailor's tie has three points. Should have two.
2. Sailor's sleeves don't match. One is short.
3. Broom-handle isn't connected to broom.
4. Hydrant is out in street. Should be on pavement.
5. Man's cuffs don't match.
6. Man's sleeves don't match.
7. Man's coat buttons on wrong side.
8. Man's left hand has six fingers.
9. Man's shoes don't match.
10. Number on building is wrong. Should be 86.
11. Sign in window is printed backwards.
12. Lamp-post isn't resting on anything.
13. Right street marker on lamp-post is off post.
14. The word "Avenue" is misspelled.
15. Top of one silo is off.
16. Awning is incomplete behind sailor.
17. Car is parked wrong on one way street.
18. Wheel on D.S.C. cart is smaller on right side.
19. D.S.C. cart cross bar handle is missing.

ARE YOU A GAGMAN?

"Of course I slapped him when he kissed me—every time!"

BRUSHOFF REBUS

MY DEAR HARRY (hare E);

YOU MISUNDERSTOOD (miss under STOOD) MY INTENTIONS (my in TENT ions) THE NIGHT BEFORE YOU DEPARTED (D parted), I'M NOT GOING (GO in G) TO BE AROUND HERE FOR LONG (4 long) SO I CAN'T REALLY (Reel-E) WAIT FOR YOU. YOUR THOUGHTS ABOUT ME (TH oughts about ME) ARE WONDERFUL (W under FUL), AND YOUR INTENTIONS (YOUR in TENT ions) MOST HONORABLE (MOST on ORABLE), BUT I'M IN LOVE WITH SOMEONE OVERSEAS (SUM—1—over C's) AND HE'LL BE BACK BEFORE VERY LONG. HE'S A HANDSOME (Hand sum) SAILOR, AN ENSIGN OVER IN EUROPE (U rope) SOMEWHERE.

DORA

GAME OF COMPARISONS

1. PALE as a ghost. 2. FRESH as a daisy. 3. NEAT as a pin. 4. SICK as a dog. 5. KEEN as a razor. 6. QUICK as a flash. 7. BROWN as a berry. 8. EASY as pie. 9. SMART as a whip. 10. HARD as nails. 11. BLIND as a bat. 12. SOBER as a judge. 13. CLEAR as a crystal. 14. STIFF as a poker. 15. FUNNY as a crutch. 16. LIGHT as a feather. 17. PRETTY as a picture. 18. FAT as a pig.

FOUR
SAILORS
PUZZLE

SHED ARM
HIRE LIE
OVAL INNS
DESIGNS
GREETS
WITHE SUE
ORATES RN
NET DOTES
TOY HEE
IDEA TEN
CORRODES

BALL AND CHAIN PUZZLE

THINK IT OVER, WAIT (TH in K, over wait) BEFORE YOU GO INTO FINAL (Fine "L") PEONAGE.

STOP AND BE WISE!

DICTIONARY DOUBLE TALK

1. Banner. 2. Barong. 3. Battlement. 4. Broad arrow. 5. Beaker. 6. Bend sinister. 7. Bellow. 8. Battle axe. 9. Beaver. 10. Bibcock. 11. Big horn. 12. Bowie knife. 13. Bonnet. 14. Busby. 15. Burin. 16. Broadsword.

ARE YOU A GAGMAN?

"That's enough politics for one night. Let's change the subject!"

DICTIONARY DOUBLE TALK

1. The QUOIN is in the building, silly!

2. Only the pears (B) could have the BLET. (A fruit disease).

3. The CABRILLA is the fish (A).

4. And the DRUGGET is the small rug (C).

5. You won't believe me but the HA-HA is the fence (A).

6. You could use the LONGE only on the horse (B).

117

SPUTNIK PROBLEM

DICTIONARY DOUBLE TALK

1. Mr. "C" is practising PANDICULATION (yawning).
2. The RUNDLET is the small barrel (B).
3. The TYCOON is the old gentleman (C).
4. The TRAGUS is the ear, not the gear (D).
5. You'll find that TUSSOCK is grass (C).
6. And you'd use PRUNELLA on the shoe, not the cereal (D).

THE EYES HAVE IT

Top line—Longest—C. Shortest—D.

Next line—Shortest—B. Longest—A and E.

Fish puzzle—Longest—the bottom one. Shortest—top.

FIGURE IT

Face. Hands (on watch). Teeth (saw). Tongue (Tong). Palms. Nails. Eardrum. Chest. Kneecap (NE-cap). Hair. Tulips (Two lips). Cords. Heart. Arch. Limb. Pupils. Locks. Arms. Soles. Bridge. Lashes. Veins. Ears. Two feet. Temple. Eyeballs. Elbow. Calf.

The rebus reads:—I POSE (P-o's) FOR NEXT TO NOTHING (4 necks 2 nothing) WITH NOTHING ON AT ALL, BUT FOR ARTISTS (4 artists) ONLY!

NUMBERS PLEASE

"M" IS FOR MACHETE

1. Machete. 2. Monogram. 3. Miter. 4. Misericord. 5. Mansard. 6. Marlinespike. 7. Minaret. 8. Mortar. 9. Mortarboard. 10. Mosquito. 11. Mosque. 12. Moulding. 13. Mask. 14. Mushrooms. 15. Millipede. 16. Manifold. 17. Mannequin. 18. Mallet.

TAKE A LETTER, DORA

Dear Dora:—

I can't understand why you are so independent (so in "D" pendant) when I am so in love. Please meet me tonight near the fire house, wait there and I'll be along before you ("A" long before "U") can say Jack Robinson. We'll take a long walk under the moon together, dance a little, and after that we can (wee can) be lovers ("L" over "S"), what do you say, Dora?

So long, darling,

Harry (Hair-"E")

CRYPTO GAG

"Never mind telling him my name—just describe me to him!"

TIPSY GYPSY

ENIGMATICAL. DEMONSTRATIONS.

THE AIRPLANE PROBLEM

The Captain's name is Smith.

CROSS
PICTURE
PUZZLE

1 N	A	3 T	4 E	■	5 S	E	W	■
6 O	M	E	N	■	7 H	O	E	■
8 T	E	N	D	■	9 E	N	D	■
10 E	N	T	I	R	E	■	S	S
■	■	■	N	O	T	■	■	T
12 S	13 T	14 A	G	E	■	15 S	16 P	A
17 P	I	N	S	■	18 B	E	A	R
19 A	R	T	■	20 P	E	A	C	E
21 R	E	S	E	T	T	L	E	S

BRIDAL WAIL

1. WEDDING (on sign) spelled wrong.
2. CHAPEAUX (on sign) wrong, too.
3. Hat is floating off chair.
4. Light fixture floating in air.
5. Chair has two different arms.
6. One leg missing on chair.
7. Word GLAMOUR is misspelled on magazine.
8. Saleslady has two different shoes.
9. She has two unmatched sleeves.
10. Her necklace is incomplete.
11. She's wearing one glove.
12. Bride has two different eyes.
13. Her veil has two unmatched fringes.
14. Her gown is incomplete in bottom fringe.
15. She shouldn't have the cuckoo on her hair.
16. She wears only one glove.
17. The tag reads SPORT SUIT.
18. The ash tray has no base.

JUNIOR WOLF

CHRYSANTHEMUM. CALCULATE.

THE TEN TRAVELERS PUZZLE

The puzzled host had put travelers One and Two in Room A. When he later removed one or the other of these to room I, he still had found no room for traveler Ten!

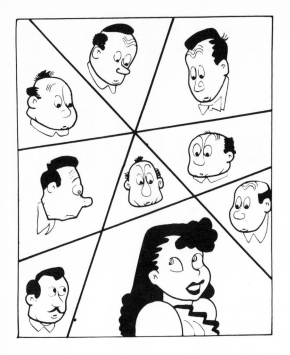

THE
EIGHT
WOLVES

"T" IS FOR TURNBUCKLE

1. Turnbuckle. 2. Tuning fork. 3. Trefoil. 4. Trapezium. 5. Turban. 6. Toucan.
7. Torii. 8. Try square. 9. Trowel. 10. Tongs. 11. Tom-tom. 12. Tomahawk. 13. Tetra-
hedron. 14. Tartan.

DICTIONARY DOUBLE TALK

1. The RAMUS is picture A. Ramus means branch.

2. If you caught the REEVE, you marked E.

3. You were wrong. The RIGOL is B.

4. The little lady with the veil is the BEGUM (B)

5. A DOWEL PIN would be used in the chair (C).

6. And the WAILING WALL is found in football (D).

"G" IS FOR GABLE

1. Gable. 2. Galleon. 3. Gannet (or Gull). 4. Gargoyle. 5. Gauntlet. 6. Gimlet.
7. Gila Monster. 8. Gouge. 9. Gopher. 10. Grampus. 11. Grapnel. 12. Griffin.
13. Grommet. 14. Governor. 15. Gastropod. 16. Gridiron. 17. Guillotine

"B" IS FOR BANNER

1. Banner. 2. Barong. 3. Battlement. 4. Broad arrow. 5. Basket. 6. Bar sinister.
7. Bellows. 8. Battle-ax. 9. Beaver. 10. Bibcock. 11. Bighorn. 12. Bowie knife.
13. Bonnet. 14. Busby. 15. Burin. 16. Broadsword.

MURDER
FOR
MYOPIA

"H" IS FOR HACKSAW

1. Hacksaw. 2. Harquebus. 3. Helmet. 4. Hexagram. 5. Heiroglyphics. 6. High-boy. 7. Hoe. 8. Hinge. 9. Handbag. 10. Hopscotch. 11. Hypotenuse. 12. Hag. 13. Hoodlum (or—Hooligan). 14. Hippopotamus.

DICTIONARY DOUBLE TALK

1. The cluster of grapes is ACINIFORM (C).
2. The BERGAMOT is the pear, believe it or not (B).
3. You'd find a PURLIN in a roof, not a snail (B).
4. A BIRKIE (B) is the man who laughs, no foolin'.
5. The RICTUS is the bird's beak (A).
6. The ACETOUS item is the bottle of vinegar (C).

CANOE UPSET

The missing word is SEASON. The sentence would read:—It was the SEASON for making love, so he rented a boat, but because of the heavy SEAS ON, he failed!

THE ROCKET FUEL PROBLEM

The clever young man was an experienced juggler. By juggling the three balls, one of them was always in the air. This left the total weight exactly 175 pounds.

FIVE VERY BUSY B's

Be backward in nothing. Be wise. Be benign. Be independent. Be honest. Be on time.

ASTIGMATIC
ADDLER

ANAGRAMGAG

The right caption is:—

"You wretch—you might have told me you were bringing somebody home to dinner!"

DICTIONARY DOUBLE TALK

1. The ZOUAVE is C.
2. The YOUNKER is B. A younker is a young gentleman or a young child.
3. The DIPSOMANIAC craves C. A dipsomaniac is a gent who craves liquor above all else.
4. The WAMPUS is B. A wampus is "a heavy, stupid, sluggish person."

"D" IS FOR DECANTER

1. Decanter. 2. Demijohn. 3. Dog. 4. Dome. 5. Doily. 6. Dormer Window. 7. Devilfish. 8. Dovetails. 9. Drill. 10. Drawknife. 11. Dividers. 12. Dolphin. 13. Dado. 14. Dory. 15. Dragoon. 16. Duet.

THE PROBLEM OF THE TWO DANCERS

The two dancing girls were two of a set of triplets.

ANAGRAMGAG

The correct gag line is:—

"Once I got started, I found I couldn't stop!"

DICTIONARY DOUBLE TALK

1. The HEDDLE is A. (A HEDDLE is a kind of rope).
2. The painter (A) would be the only man who uses PARGET.
3. You'll find the INION in the back of the man's head (C).
4. The KOORAJONG is B—(a mountain—or hill).

TWO IS COMPANY

Mutt and Jeff. Laurel and Hardy. Antony (Ant on "E") and Cleopatra. Wheeler and Woolsey. Castor and Pollux. Weber and Fields. Darby and Joan. Pick and Pat. Punch and Judy. Cain and Abel. Potash and Perlmutter. Beaumont and Fletcher. Popeye and Olive Oil. Hansel and Gretel. Sacco and Venzetti.

LITERARY IMPASSE

The only three letter word to be formed from the letters on the dials is:—PYX. (You'll find it in the dictionary—no foolin'). And the anagram is: ADMINISTRATION.

DICTIONARY DOUBLE-TALK

1. The vase (D) is SEME—(covered with stars).
2. The TOD is the small clump of bushes—(A).
3. The VIMEN is the branch—believe it or not!
4. The CARLINE is the old lady—(C).
5. The FAL-LAL is the ornament on the girl's dress—(B).

KISS
ME
QUICK

124

THE PUZZLE OF THE HOLLYWOOD STARLETS

The first girl was a STAR.

The second girl was a STAR.

The third girl was a STARLET.

The first girl undoubtedly said, "I am a Star." (If she were a Star, she would have told the truth. Contrariwise, if she were a Starlet, she would have lied and said she was a Star.)

The second girl who reported the first girl as saying she was a Star must have then been telling the truth about what she heard. (Thus, the second girl must be a Star, too. Since her remark was true, it stands to reason that the first girl must be a Star.)

The third girl, therefore, since she reported the second girl as being a Starlet, was obviously lying. She must therefore be a Starlet herself.

SUITOR'S SURPRISE

1. Girl's shoes are different.
2. Doorknob is too low.
3. LIBERTY is spelled wrong on magazine.
4. Girl's left hand has six fingers.
5. Girl's collar is different on both sides.
6. Man's tie is off his collar.
7. His left hand has only four fingers.
8. His left cuff has three buttons.
9. His side pocket is too far back on his jacket.
10. He's been wearing two pairs of glasses.
11. The glasses on his face don't fit to his ears.
12. Clock on wall has three hands.
13. Picture is out of frame.
14. One of the pendulums is unattached.
15. Lamp shade is floating in air.
16. Ditto for glass of water.
17. Lamp is plugged into man's leg. (Shocking!)
18. Liquor glass has no bottom.
19. Pipe has no stem.
20. Table has no leg on left side.

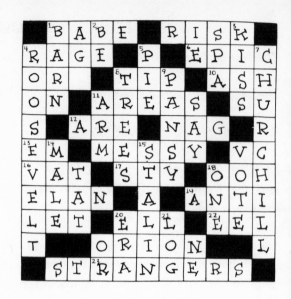

CROSS
PICTURE
PUZZLE

HOW FUNNY ARE YOU?

"If you must know—it fell off a desk!"

TEST YOUR FUNNY BONE

If your sense of humor is perfect, these were your choices:—

2—3—6

DICTIONARY DOUBLE TALK

1. The ORLOP is in picture D—it's part of a boat, not an oar.
2. The NEEP is item C—a turnip.
3. The MERCER is the man holding the cloth.
4. The chain is the CATENATED object.

PAIR 'EM UP

2. Tristan and Isolde. (T—wrist—An). 3. Paolo (Pail—O) and Franscesca. 4. Pygmalion (Pig—male—ion) and Galatea. 5. Jack and Jill. 6. Alphonse (Alph— on SE) and Gaston. 7. Ferdinand and Isabella. 8. Dante (D—ant—E) and Beatrice. 9. Archy (Arch—E) and Mehitabel. 10. Venus (V in US) and Adonis. 11. Molasses (Mo—Lass—S) and January. 12. Evangeline (E—van—G—line) and Gabriel. 13. Blondie (Bl on D) and Dagwood. 14. Burns (Burn—"S") and Allen.— 15. Block and Sully (or—Tackle).

ANAGRAMGAG

The correct caption is:—

"He's got the wrong number—anybody want to speak to him?"

FISHERMAN'S FUN

Your funny bone should have reacted this way for a perfect score:—3—1—6.

CRYPTOGAG

"What's wrong? You said you wanted the money for coffee, didn't you?"

QUICK PICK

Mrs. Friditch can spend the $50 by selecting items costing $19, $6, and $25.

ADJECTIVITY

1. Serpentine. 2. Canine. 3. Avine. 4. Leporine. 5. Bovine. 6. Porcine. 7. Ciconine. 8. Piscine. 9. Ursine. 10. Lacertine. 11. Formicine.

SCRAMBLED CORN

The correct gag line is:

"But, gentlemen, it was just a lucky catch—and anyway, I've GOT a job!"

HOW FUNNY ARE YOU?

"Why aren't you in the movies?"

THE
MALVERNE
MAZE

"S" IS FOR SABOT

1. Sabot. 2. Sampan. 3. Scimitar. 4. Semaphore. 5. Shuttlecock. 6. Scythe. 7. Shako. 8. Sickle. 9. Sloth. 10. Spatula. 11. Spearhead. 12. Sombrero. 13. Starfish. 14. Swordfish. 15. Staple. 16. Spiral. 17. Silhouette.

THE BODY BEAUTIFUL

Auricle—ear. Myocardium—heart. Epidermis—skin. Conjuctiva—eye. Bronchi—chest, lungs. Digit—finger. Pharynx—throat. Peritoneum—abdomen. Cerebrum—brain. Ilium—hip. Denture—teeth. Os—mouth, or bone.

GOOD HUMOR TEST

"Joe—I want you to meet the little woman!"

"C" IS FOR CADUCEUS

1. Caduceus. 2. Calabash. 3. Canthook. 4. Canton. 5. Capstan. 6. Calipers. 7. Castle. 8. Catboat. 9. Calumet. 10. Chalice. 11. Cleaver. 12. Clamp. 13. Clef. 14. Coping. 15. Cleat. 16. Creese. 17. Cowl.

MORNING MYSTERY

PANORAMA.

THE NAUGHTICAL NOUGHTS

Odd gob. Good dog.

SMALL CHANGE

Fire — fore — FORD — cord — cold.   Ride — WIDE — wade — walk.

A CHANGE OF CLIMATE

North — FORTH — forts — TORTS — toots — tooth — SOOTH — south.

NINE MOVE WORD CHANGE

Soup — sour — pour — pout — post — past — FAST — fist — fish.

CRYPTOGAG

"Never mind telling him my name — just describe me to him!"

CRYPTOGAG (Page 107)

"Let's don't sit near the water — I've got a friend on a submarine somewhere!"